# THIS BOOK BELONGS TO:

# PHARMACOLOGY Notes

Class

## INDICATIONS

## Generic name        Trade name

## PATIENT TEACHING

## NURSING CONSIDERATIONS

## CONTRAINDICATIONS

## MECHANISM OF ACTION

## SIDE EFFECTS

## Notes

# PHARMACOLOGY Notes

Class _____

## INDICATIONS

## GENERIC NAME          TRADE NAME

## PATIENT TEACHING

## NURSING CONSIDERATIONS

## CONTRAINDICATIONS

## MECHANISM OF ACTION

## SIDE EFFECTS

## Notes

# PHARMACOLOGY Notes

Class

## INDICATIONS

## GENERIC NAME     TRADE NAME

## PATIENT TEACHING

## NURSING CONSIDERATIONS

## CONTRAINDICATIONS

## MECHANISM OF ACTION

## SIDE EFFECTS

## NOTES

# PHARMACOLOGY Notes

Class

### INDICATIONS

### Generic name    Trade name

### PATIENT TEACHING

### NURSING CONSIDERATIONS

### CONTRAINDICATIONS

### MECHANISM OF ACTION

### SIDE EFFECTS

### Notes

# PHARMACOLOGY NOTES

Class

### INDICATIONS

### GENERIC NAME          TRADE NAME

### PATIENT TEACHING

### NURSING CONSIDERATIONS

### CONTRAINDICATIONS

### MECHANISM OF ACTION

### SIDE EFFECTS

### NOTES

# PHARMACOLOGY Notes

Class

## INDICATIONS

## GENERIC NAME    TRADE NAME

## PATIENT TEACHING

## NURSING CONSIDERATIONS

## CONTRAINDICATIONS

## MECHANISM OF ACTION

## SIDE EFFECTS

## NOTES

# PHARMACOLOGY Notes

Class

| INDICATIONS | GENERIC NAME | TRADE NAME |
|---|---|---|

PATIENT TEACHING

NURSING CONSIDERATIONS

CONTRAINDICATIONS

MECHANISM OF ACTION

SIDE EFFECTS

NOTES

# PHARMACOLOGY Notes

Class

## INDICATIONS

## Generic name          Trade name

## PATIENT TEACHING

## NURSING CONSIDERATIONS

## CONTRAINDICATIONS

## MECHANISM OF ACTION

## SIDE EFFECTS

## Notes

# PHARMACOLOGY Notes

Class

## INDICATIONS

## GENERIC NAME      TRADE NAME

## PATIENT TEACHING

## NURSING CONSIDERATIONS

## CONTRAINDICATIONS

## MECHANISM OF ACTION

## SIDE EFFECTS

## Notes

# PHARMACOLOGY Notes

Class

## INDICATIONS

## GENERIC NAME          TRADE NAME

## PATIENT TEACHING

## NURSING CONSIDERATIONS

## CONTRAINDICATIONS

## MECHANISM OF ACTION

## SIDE EFFECTS

## NOTES

# PHARMACOLOGY Notes

Class

INDICATIONS

GENERIC NAME          TRADE NAME

PATIENT TEACHING

NURSING CONSIDERATIONS

CONTRAINDICATIONS

MECHANISM OF ACTION

SIDE EFFECTS

NOTES

# PHARMACOLOGY Notes

Class

## INDICATIONS

## GENERIC NAME    TRADE NAME

## PATIENT TEACHING

## NURSING CONSIDERATIONS

## CONTRAINDICATIONS

## MECHANISM OF ACTION

## SIDE EFFECTS

## Notes

# PHARMACOLOGY Notes

Class

## INDICATIONS

## GENERIC NAME    TRADE NAME

## PATIENT TEACHING

## NURSING CONSIDERATIONS

## CONTRAINDICATIONS

## MECHANISM OF ACTION

## SIDE EFFECTS

## Notes

# PHARMACOLOGY Notes

Class

## INDICATIONS

## GENERIC NAME        TRADE NAME

## PATIENT TEACHING

## NURSING CONSIDERATIONS

## CONTRAINDICATIONS

## MECHANISM OF ACTION

## SIDE EFFECTS

## NOTES

# PHARMACOLOGY Notes

Class

### INDICATIONS

### GENERIC NAME          TRADE NAME

### PATIENT TEACHING

### NURSING CONSIDERATIONS

### CONTRAINDICATIONS

### MECHANISM OF ACTION

### SIDE EFFECTS

### NOTES

# PHARMACOLOGY Notes

Class

## INDICATIONS

## GENERIC NAME          TRADE NAME

## PATIENT TEACHING

## NURSING CONSIDERATIONS

## CONTRAINDICATIONS

## MECHANISM OF ACTION

## SIDE EFFECTS

## Notes

# PHARMACOLOGY Notes

Class

## INDICATIONS

## GENERIC NAME        TRADE NAME

## PATIENT TEACHING

## NURSING CONSIDERATIONS

## CONTRAINDICATIONS

## MECHANISM OF ACTION

## SIDE EFFECTS

## NOTES

# PHARMACOLOGY Notes

Class

## INDICATIONS

## GENERIC NAME        TRADE NAME

## PATIENT TEACHING

## NURSING CONSIDERATIONS

## CONTRAINDICATIONS

## MECHANISM OF ACTION

## SIDE EFFECTS

## NOTES

# PHARMACOLOGY Notes

Class

## INDICATIONS

## GENERIC NAME          TRADE NAME

## PATIENT TEACHING

## NURSING CONSIDERATIONS

## CONTRAINDICATIONS

## MECHANISM OF ACTION

## SIDE EFFECTS

## Notes

# PHARMACOLOGY Notes

Class

## INDICATIONS

## GENERIC NAME          TRADE NAME

## PATIENT TEACHING

## NURSING CONSIDERATIONS

## CONTRAINDICATIONS

## MECHANISM OF ACTION

## SIDE EFFECTS

## Notes

# PHARMACOLOGY Notes

Class

## INDICATIONS

## GENERIC NAME          TRADE NAME

## PATIENT TEACHING

## NURSING CONSIDERATIONS

## CONTRAINDICATIONS

## MECHANISM OF ACTION

## SIDE EFFECTS

## Notes

# PHARMACOLOGY Notes

Class

## INDICATIONS

## GENERIC NAME          TRADE NAME

## PATIENT TEACHING

## NURSING CONSIDERATIONS

## CONTRAINDICATIONS

## MECHANISM OF ACTION

## SIDE EFFECTS

## NOTES

# PHARMACOLOGY Notes

Class

### INDICATIONS

### GENERIC NAME          TRADE NAME

### PATIENT TEACHING

### NURSING CONSIDERATIONS

### CONTRAINDICATIONS

### MECHANISM OF ACTION

### SIDE EFFECTS

### NOTES

# PHARMACOLOGY Notes

Class

## INDICATIONS

## GENERIC NAME          TRADE NAME

## PATIENT TEACHING

## NURSING CONSIDERATIONS

## CONTRAINDICATIONS

## MECHANISM OF ACTION

## SIDE EFFECTS

## Notes

# PHARMACOLOGY Notes

Class

## INDICATIONS

## GENERIC NAME        TRADE NAME

## PATIENT TEACHING

## NURSING CONSIDERATIONS

## CONTRAINDICATIONS

## MECHANISM OF ACTION

## SIDE EFFECTS

## NOTES

# PHARMACOLOGY Notes

Class _____

## INDICATIONS

## GENERIC NAME          TRADE NAME

## PATIENT TEACHING

## NURSING CONSIDERATIONS

## CONTRAINDICATIONS

## MECHANISM OF ACTION

## SIDE EFFECTS

## NOTES

# PHARMACOLOGY Notes

Class

### INDICATIONS

### GENERIC NAME          TRADE NAME

### PATIENT TEACHING

### NURSING CONSIDERATIONS

### CONTRAINDICATIONS

### MECHANISM OF ACTION

### SIDE EFFECTS

### NOTES

# PHARMACOLOGY Notes

Class

## INDICATIONS

## Generic name          Trade name

## PATIENT TEACHING

## NURSING CONSIDERATIONS

## CONTRAINDICATIONS

## MECHANISM OF ACTION

## SIDE EFFECTS

## Notes

# PHARMACOLOGY Notes

Class

## INDICATIONS

## GENERIC NAME     TRADE NAME

## PATIENT TEACHING

## NURSING CONSIDERATIONS

## CONTRAINDICATIONS

## MECHANISM OF ACTION

## SIDE EFFECTS

## NOTES

# PHARMACOLOGY Notes

Class

## INDICATIONS

## GENERIC NAME          TRADE NAME

## PATIENT TEACHING

## NURSING CONSIDERATIONS

## CONTRAINDICATIONS

## MECHANISM OF ACTION

## SIDE EFFECTS

## NOTES

# PHARMACOLOGY Notes

Class

## INDICATIONS

## GENERIC NAME          TRADE NAME

## PATIENT TEACHING

## NURSING CONSIDERATIONS

## CONTRAINDICATIONS

## MECHANISM OF ACTION

## SIDE EFFECTS

## Notes

# PHARMACOLOGY Notes

Class

## INDICATIONS

## GENERIC NAME          TRADE NAME

## PATIENT TEACHING

## NURSING CONSIDERATIONS

## CONTRAINDICATIONS

## MECHANISM OF ACTION

## SIDE EFFECTS

## Notes

# PHARMACOLOGY Notes

Class

## INDICATIONS

## GENERIC NAME        TRADE NAME

## PATIENT TEACHING

## NURSING CONSIDERATIONS

## CONTRAINDICATIONS

## MECHANISM OF ACTION

## SIDE EFFECTS

## Notes

# PHARMACOLOGY Notes

Class

## INDICATIONS

## GENERIC NAME          TRADE NAME

## PATIENT TEACHING

## NURSING CONSIDERATIONS

## CONTRAINDICATIONS

## MECHANISM OF ACTION

## SIDE EFFECTS

## NOTES

# PHARMACOLOGY Notes

Class

## INDICATIONS

## GENERIC NAME          TRADE NAME

## PATIENT TEACHING

## NURSING CONSIDERATIONS

## CONTRAINDICATIONS

## MECHANISM OF ACTION

## SIDE EFFECTS

## Notes

# PHARMACOLOGY Notes

Class

## INDICATIONS

## GENERIC NAME          TRADE NAME

## PATIENT TEACHING

## NURSING CONSIDERATIONS

## CONTRAINDICATIONS

## MECHANISM OF ACTION

## SIDE EFFECTS

## Notes

# PHARMACOLOGY Notes

Class

### INDICATIONS

### GENERIC NAME          TRADE NAME

### PATIENT TEACHING

### NURSING CONSIDERATIONS

### CONTRAINDICATIONS

### MECHANISM OF ACTION

### SIDE EFFECTS

### Notes

# PHARMACOLOGY Notes

Class

## INDICATIONS

## GENERIC NAME          TRADE NAME

## PATIENT TEACHING

## NURSING CONSIDERATIONS

## CONTRAINDICATIONS

## MECHANISM OF ACTION

## SIDE EFFECTS

## Notes

# PHARMACOLOGY Notes

Class

## INDICATIONS

## GENERIC NAME    TRADE NAME

## PATIENT TEACHING

## NURSING CONSIDERATIONS

## CONTRAINDICATIONS

## MECHANISM OF ACTION

## SIDE EFFECTS

Notes

# PHARMACOLOGY Notes

Class

## INDICATIONS

## GENERIC NAME          TRADE NAME

## PATIENT TEACHING

## NURSING CONSIDERATIONS

## CONTRAINDICATIONS

## MECHANISM OF ACTION

## SIDE EFFECTS

## Notes

# PHARMACOLOGY Notes

Class

## INDICATIONS

## GENERIC NAME    TRADE NAME

## PATIENT TEACHING

## NURSING CONSIDERATIONS

## CONTRAINDICATIONS

## MECHANISM OF ACTION

## SIDE EFFECTS

## Notes

# PHARMACOLOGY Notes

Class

## INDICATIONS

## GENERIC NAME        TRADE NAME

## PATIENT TEACHING

## NURSING CONSIDERATIONS

## CONTRAINDICATIONS

## MECHANISM OF ACTION

## SIDE EFFECTS

## Notes

# PHARMACOLOGY Notes

Class

## INDICATIONS

## GENERIC NAME      TRADE NAME

## PATIENT TEACHING

## NURSING CONSIDERATIONS

## CONTRAINDICATIONS

## MECHANISM OF ACTION

## SIDE EFFECTS

## Notes

# PHARMACOLOGY Notes

Class

## INDICATIONS

## GENERIC NAME      TRADE NAME

## PATIENT TEACHING

## NURSING CONSIDERATIONS

## CONTRAINDICATIONS

## MECHANISM OF ACTION

## SIDE EFFECTS

## Notes

# PHARMACOLOGY Notes

Class

## INDICATIONS

## GENERIC NAME          TRADE NAME

## PATIENT TEACHING

## NURSING CONSIDERATIONS

## CONTRAINDICATIONS

## MECHANISM OF ACTION

## SIDE EFFECTS

Notes

# PHARMACOLOGY Notes

Class

## INDICATIONS

## GENERIC NAME          TRADE NAME

## PATIENT TEACHING

## NURSING CONSIDERATIONS

## CONTRAINDICATIONS

## MECHANISM OF ACTION

## SIDE EFFECTS

## Notes

# PHARMACOLOGY Notes

Class

## INDICATIONS

## GENERIC NAME     TRADE NAME

## PATIENT TEACHING

## NURSING CONSIDERATIONS

## CONTRAINDICATIONS

## MECHANISM OF ACTION

## SIDE EFFECTS

## Notes

# PHARMACOLOGY Notes

Class

## INDICATIONS

## GENERIC NAME          TRADE NAME

## PATIENT TEACHING

## NURSING CONSIDERATIONS

## CONTRAINDICATIONS

## MECHANISM OF ACTION

## SIDE EFFECTS

## Notes

# PHARMACOLOGY Notes

Class

## INDICATIONS

## GENERIC NAME        TRADE NAME

## PATIENT TEACHING

## NURSING CONSIDERATIONS

## CONTRAINDICATIONS

## MECHANISM OF ACTION

## SIDE EFFECTS

Notes

# PHARMACOLOGY Notes

Class

## INDICATIONS

## GENERIC NAME          TRADE NAME

## PATIENT TEACHING

## NURSING CONSIDERATIONS

## CONTRAINDICATIONS

## MECHANISM OF ACTION

## SIDE EFFECTS

Notes

# PHARMACOLOGY Notes

Class

## INDICATIONS

## GENERIC NAME          TRADE NAME

## PATIENT TEACHING

## NURSING CONSIDERATIONS

## CONTRAINDICATIONS

## MECHANISM OF ACTION

## SIDE EFFECTS

Notes

# PHARMACOLOGY Notes

Class

## INDICATIONS

## GENERIC NAME          TRADE NAME

## PATIENT TEACHING

## NURSING CONSIDERATIONS

## CONTRAINDICATIONS

## MECHANISM OF ACTION

## SIDE EFFECTS

## Notes

# PHARMACOLOGY Notes

Class

### INDICATIONS

### GENERIC NAME     TRADE NAME

### PATIENT TEACHING

### NURSING CONSIDERATIONS

### CONTRAINDICATIONS

### MECHANISM OF ACTION

### SIDE EFFECTS

Notes

# PHARMACOLOGY NOTES

Class

## INDICATIONS

## GENERIC NAME    TRADE NAME

## PATIENT TEACHING

## NURSING CONSIDERATIONS

## CONTRAINDICATIONS

## MECHANISM OF ACTION

## SIDE EFFECTS

## NOTES

# PHARMACOLOGY Notes

Class

| INDICATIONS | GENERIC NAME    TRADE NAME |
| --- | --- |
| | PATIENT TEACHING |

| NURSING CONSIDERATIONS | CONTRAINDICATIONS |
| --- | --- |

| MECHANISM OF ACTION | SIDE EFFECTS |
| --- | --- |

Notes

# PHARMACOLOGY Notes

Class

## INDICATIONS

## GENERIC NAME          TRADE NAME

## PATIENT TEACHING

## NURSING CONSIDERATIONS

## CONTRAINDICATIONS

## MECHANISM OF ACTION

## SIDE EFFECTS

## Notes

# PHARMACOLOGY Notes

Class

## INDICATIONS

## GENERIC NAME        TRADE NAME

## PATIENT TEACHING

## NURSING CONSIDERATIONS

## CONTRAINDICATIONS

## MECHANISM OF ACTION

## SIDE EFFECTS

## Notes

# PHARMACOLOGY Notes

Class

## INDICATIONS

## GENERIC NAME          TRADE NAME

## PATIENT TEACHING

## NURSING CONSIDERATIONS

## CONTRAINDICATIONS

## MECHANISM OF ACTION

## SIDE EFFECTS

## NOTES

# Pharmacology Notes

Class

## Indications

## Generic name    Trade name

## Patient teaching

## Nursing considerations

## Contraindications

## Mechanism of action

## Side effects

## Notes

# PHARMACOLOGY Notes

Class

## INDICATIONS

## GENERIC NAME          TRADE NAME

## PATIENT TEACHING

## NURSING CONSIDERATIONS

## CONTRAINDICATIONS

## MECHANISM OF ACTION

## SIDE EFFECTS

## NOTES

# PHARMACOLOGY Notes

Class

### INDICATIONS

### GENERIC NAME     TRADE NAME

### PATIENT TEACHING

### NURSING CONSIDERATIONS

### CONTRAINDICATIONS

### MECHANISM OF ACTION

### SIDE EFFECTS

Notes

# PHARMACOLOGY NOTES

Class

## INDICATIONS

## GENERIC NAME     TRADE NAME

## PATIENT TEACHING

## NURSING CONSIDERATIONS

## CONTRAINDICATIONS

## MECHANISM OF ACTION

## SIDE EFFECTS

## NOTES

# PHARMACOLOGY Notes

Class

## INDICATIONS

## GENERIC NAME    TRADE NAME

## PATIENT TEACHING

## NURSING CONSIDERATIONS

## CONTRAINDICATIONS

## MECHANISM OF ACTION

## SIDE EFFECTS

Notes

# PHARMACOLOGY Notes

Class

## INDICATIONS

## GENERIC NAME     TRADE NAME

## PATIENT TEACHING

## NURSING CONSIDERATIONS

## CONTRAINDICATIONS

## MECHANISM OF ACTION

## SIDE EFFECTS

## NOTES

# PHARMACOLOGY Notes

Class

### INDICATIONS

### GENERIC NAME          TRADE NAME

### PATIENT TEACHING

### NURSING CONSIDERATIONS

### CONTRAINDICATIONS

### MECHANISM OF ACTION

### SIDE EFFECTS

### NOTES

# PHARMACOLOGY Notes

Class

## INDICATIONS

## GENERIC NAME     TRADE NAME

## PATIENT TEACHING

## NURSING CONSIDERATIONS

## CONTRAINDICATIONS

## MECHANISM OF ACTION

## SIDE EFFECTS

## Notes

# Pharmacology Notes

Class

| INDICATIONS | GENERIC NAME | TRADE NAME |
|---|---|---|

## PATIENT TEACHING

## NURSING CONSIDERATIONS

## CONTRAINDICATIONS

## MECHANISM OF ACTION

## SIDE EFFECTS

## Notes

# PHARMACOLOGY Notes

Class

## INDICATIONS

## GENERIC NAME          TRADE NAME

## PATIENT TEACHING

## NURSING CONSIDERATIONS

## CONTRAINDICATIONS

## MECHANISM OF ACTION

## SIDE EFFECTS

## Notes

# PHARMACOLOGY Notes

Class

## INDICATIONS

## GENERIC NAME    TRADE NAME

## PATIENT TEACHING

## NURSING CONSIDERATIONS

## CONTRAINDICATIONS

## MECHANISM OF ACTION

## SIDE EFFECTS

## Notes

# PHARMACOLOGY Notes

Class

## INDICATIONS

## GENERIC NAME        TRADE NAME

## PATIENT TEACHING

## NURSING CONSIDERATIONS

## CONTRAINDICATIONS

## MECHANISM OF ACTION

## SIDE EFFECTS

## Notes

# PHARMACOLOGY Notes

Class

## INDICATIONS

## GENERIC NAME          TRADE NAME

## PATIENT TEACHING

## NURSING CONSIDERATIONS

## CONTRAINDICATIONS

## MECHANISM OF ACTION

## SIDE EFFECTS

## Notes

# PHARMACOLOGY Notes

Class

## INDICATIONS

## GENERIC NAME          TRADE NAME

## PATIENT TEACHING

## NURSING CONSIDERATIONS

## CONTRAINDICATIONS

## MECHANISM OF ACTION

## SIDE EFFECTS

## Notes

# PHARMACOLOGY Notes

Class

### INDICATIONS

### GENERIC NAME     TRADE NAME

### PATIENT TEACHING

### NURSING CONSIDERATIONS

### CONTRAINDICATIONS

### MECHANISM OF ACTION

### SIDE EFFECTS

Notes

# PHARMACOLOGY NOTES

Class

| INDICATIONS | GENERIC NAME | TRADE NAME |
|---|---|---|

### PATIENT TEACHING

### NURSING CONSIDERATIONS

### CONTRAINDICATIONS

### MECHANISM OF ACTION

### SIDE EFFECTS

### Notes

# PHARMACOLOGY Notes

Class

## INDICATIONS

## GENERIC NAME          TRADE NAME

## PATIENT TEACHING

## NURSING CONSIDERATIONS

## CONTRAINDICATIONS

## MECHANISM OF ACTION

## SIDE EFFECTS

## Notes

# PHARMACOLOGY Notes

Class

## INDICATIONS

## GENERIC NAME          TRADE NAME

## PATIENT TEACHING

## NURSING CONSIDERATIONS

## CONTRAINDICATIONS

## MECHANISM OF ACTION

## SIDE EFFECTS

## NOTES

# PHARMACOLOGY Notes

Class

## INDICATIONS

## GENERIC NAME          TRADE NAME

## PATIENT TEACHING

## NURSING CONSIDERATIONS

## CONTRAINDICATIONS

## MECHANISM OF ACTION

## SIDE EFFECTS

## NOTES

# PHARMACOLOGY Notes

Class

## INDICATIONS

## GENERIC NAME     TRADE NAME

## PATIENT TEACHING

## NURSING CONSIDERATIONS

## CONTRAINDICATIONS

## MECHANISM OF ACTION

## SIDE EFFECTS

## Notes

# Pharmacology Notes

Class

## INDICATIONS

## GENERIC NAME  TRADE NAME

## PATIENT TEACHING

## NURSING CONSIDERATIONS

## CONTRAINDICATIONS

## MECHANISM OF ACTION

## SIDE EFFECTS

## Notes

# PHARMACOLOGY Notes

Class

### INDICATIONS

### GENERIC NAME    TRADE NAME

### PATIENT TEACHING

### NURSING CONSIDERATIONS

### CONTRAINDICATIONS

### MECHANISM OF ACTION

### SIDE EFFECTS

### Notes

# PHARMACOLOGY Notes

Class

## INDICATIONS

## GENERIC NAME          TRADE NAME

## PATIENT TEACHING

## NURSING CONSIDERATIONS

## CONTRAINDICATIONS

## MECHANISM OF ACTION

## SIDE EFFECTS

## NOTES

# PHARMACOLOGY Notes

Class

## INDICATIONS

## GENERIC NAME          TRADE NAME

## PATIENT TEACHING

## NURSING CONSIDERATIONS

## CONTRAINDICATIONS

## MECHANISM OF ACTION

## SIDE EFFECTS

## Notes

# PHARMACOLOGY Notes

Class

## INDICATIONS

## GENERIC NAME        TRADE NAME

## PATIENT TEACHING

## NURSING CONSIDERATIONS

## CONTRAINDICATIONS

## MECHANISM OF ACTION

## SIDE EFFECTS

## Notes

# PHARMACOLOGY NOTES

Class

### INDICATIONS

### GENERIC NAME     TRADE NAME

### PATIENT TEACHING

### NURSING CONSIDERATIONS

### CONTRAINDICATIONS

### MECHANISM OF ACTION

### SIDE EFFECTS

Notes

# PHARMACOLOGY Notes

Class

## INDICATIONS

## GENERIC NAME          TRADE NAME

## PATIENT TEACHING

## NURSING CONSIDERATIONS

## CONTRAINDICATIONS

## MECHANISM OF ACTION

## SIDE EFFECTS

## Notes

# PHARMACOLOGY NOTES

Class

## INDICATIONS

## GENERIC NAME          TRADE NAME

## PATIENT TEACHING

## NURSING CONSIDERATIONS

## CONTRAINDICATIONS

## MECHANISM OF ACTION

## SIDE EFFECTS

## NOTES

# PHARMACOLOGY Notes

Class

| INDICATIONS | GENERIC NAME | TRADE NAME |
| --- | --- | --- |

### PATIENT TEACHING

### NURSING CONSIDERATIONS

### CONTRAINDICATIONS

### MECHANISM OF ACTION

### SIDE EFFECTS

### Notes

# PHARMACOLOGY Notes

Class

## INDICATIONS

## GENERIC NAME          TRADE NAME

## PATIENT TEACHING

## NURSING CONSIDERATIONS

## CONTRAINDICATIONS

## MECHANISM OF ACTION

## SIDE EFFECTS

## Notes

# PHARMACOLOGY Notes

Class

## INDICATIONS

## GENERIC NAME        TRADE NAME

## PATIENT TEACHING

## NURSING CONSIDERATIONS

## CONTRAINDICATIONS

## MECHANISM OF ACTION

## SIDE EFFECTS

## NOTES

# PHARMACOLOGY Notes

Class

## INDICATIONS

## GENERIC NAME          TRADE NAME

## PATIENT TEACHING

## NURSING CONSIDERATIONS

## CONTRAINDICATIONS

## MECHANISM OF ACTION

## SIDE EFFECTS

## Notes

# PHARMACOLOGY Notes

Class

## INDICATIONS

## GENERIC NAME          TRADE NAME

## PATIENT TEACHING

## NURSING CONSIDERATIONS

## CONTRAINDICATIONS

## MECHANISM OF ACTION

## SIDE EFFECTS

## NOTES

# PHARMACOLOGY Notes

Class

## INDICATIONS

## GENERIC NAME          TRADE NAME

## PATIENT TEACHING

## NURSING CONSIDERATIONS

## CONTRAINDICATIONS

## MECHANISM OF ACTION

## SIDE EFFECTS

## Notes

# PHARMACOLOGY Notes

Class

## INDICATIONS

## GENERIC NAME          TRADE NAME

## PATIENT TEACHING

## NURSING CONSIDERATIONS

## CONTRAINDICATIONS

## MECHANISM OF ACTION

## SIDE EFFECTS

## NOTES

# PHARMACOLOGY Notes

Class

## INDICATIONS

## GENERIC NAME      TRADE NAME

## PATIENT TEACHING

## NURSING CONSIDERATIONS

## CONTRAINDICATIONS

## MECHANISM OF ACTION

## SIDE EFFECTS

## NOTES

# PHARMACOLOGY Notes

Class

### INDICATIONS

### GENERIC NAME          TRADE NAME

### PATIENT TEACHING

### NURSING CONSIDERATIONS

### CONTRAINDICATIONS

### MECHANISM OF ACTION

### SIDE EFFECTS

### Notes

# PHARMACOLOGY Notes

Class

## INDICATIONS

## GENERIC NAME          TRADE NAME

## PATIENT TEACHING

## NURSING CONSIDERATIONS

## CONTRAINDICATIONS

## MECHANISM OF ACTION

## SIDE EFFECTS

## Notes

# PHARMACOLOGY Notes

Class

## INDICATIONS

## GENERIC NAME        TRADE NAME

## PATIENT TEACHING

## NURSING CONSIDERATIONS

## CONTRAINDICATIONS

## MECHANISM OF ACTION

## SIDE EFFECTS

## Notes

# PHARMACOLOGY Notes

Class

## INDICATIONS

## GENERIC NAME     TRADE NAME

## PATIENT TEACHING

## NURSING CONSIDERATIONS

## CONTRAINDICATIONS

## MECHANISM OF ACTION

## SIDE EFFECTS

## Notes

# PHARMACOLOGY Notes

Class

## INDICATIONS

## GENERIC NAME          TRADE NAME

## PATIENT TEACHING

## NURSING CONSIDERATIONS

## CONTRAINDICATIONS

## MECHANISM OF ACTION

## SIDE EFFECTS

## NOTES

Made in the USA
Monee, IL
30 December 2022

24071154R00057